I am lāt<sub>e</sub>. I āt<sub>e</sub> ham on a hill.

I āt<sub>e</sub> and āt<sub>e</sub>. and now I am

lāt<sub>e</sub>. I will run.

1

hē has a fat cat. hē has fun with his fat cat.

his mom has a littlₑ cat. shē has fun with thē littlₑ cat. thē littlₑ cat has fun in thē sand.

a littl<sub>e</sub> fish sat on a fat fish.

thē littl<sub>e</sub> fish said, "wow."

thē littl<sub>e</sub> fish did not hāt<sub>e</sub> thē

fat fish. thē littl<sub>e</sub> fish said,

"that fat fish is mom."

a fish āt_e a roc_k. thē fish

said, "I āt_e a roc_k."

a cow āt_e thē fish. thē cow

said, "I āt_e a fish. and now I

fēēl sic_k."

shē was not mad at him. did

shē hit him? nō, nō, nō. did shē

hug him? nō, nō, nō. did shē

kiss him?

hē has nō fēēt. hē has nō

nōsₑ. hē has nō tēēth. hē is not

a cow. and hē is not a cat.

is hē a rat? nō. hē is not a

rat.

I hav_e a cow. thē cow is fat.

I hav_e a cat. thē cat is fat.

how can I tāk_e thē cow and

thē cat with mē? can thē cow

sit on thē cat? nō.

wē sāv<sub>e</sub> roc<sub>k</sub>s. wē sāv<sub>e</sub> sac<sub>k</sub>s

and sac<sub>k</sub>s of roc<sub>k</sub>s. wē sāv<sub>e</sub>

lots and lots of roc<sub>k</sub>s.

wē hav<sub>e</sub> lots of littl<sub>e</sub> roc<sub>k</sub>s.

wē sit on roc<sub>k</sub>s. and wē giv<sub>e</sub>

an ōld man lots of roc<sub>k</sub>s.

the ōld man said, "I can shāve a cat." sō hē did.

the ōld man said, "I can shāve a cow." sō hē did.

the ōld man said, "I can shāve a rock."

did hē shāv<sub>e</sub> a roc<sub>k</sub>? nō.

hē said, "givₑ mē a hat ōr a socₖ." sō shē gāvₑ him a socₖ fōr his nōsₑ.

hē said, "I nēēd socₖs on thē fēēt, not on thē nōsₑ." sō shē gāvₑ him socₖs fōr his fēēt.

the ōld gōat had an ōld cōat.

the ōld gōat said, "I will ēat this

ōld cōat." sō shē did.

"that was fun," shē said. "I āte

the ōld cōat. and now I am cōld."

now the ōld gōat is sad.

thē rat had fun. hē ran in

thē sand.

hē had sand on his fēēt. hē

had sand on his ērs. hē had

sand on his nōse. hē had sand

on his tāil.

hē said, "I haVe a lot of sand

on mē."

a dog sat in a littlₑ car. thē

dog said, "I nēēd to ēₐt."

will thē dog ēₐt a fish? nō.

will thē dog ēₐt a log? nō. will

thē dog ēₐt a pot of tar? nō.

thē dog will ēₐt thē car.

# lots of cars

a man on a farm has lots of

cars. hē has ōld cars. hē has

littlₑ cars.

arₑ his cars fōr gōₐts? nō.

arₑ his cars fōr shēēp? nō. arₑ

his cars fōr cows? nō.

his cars arₑ fōr cops. hē has

lots of cop cars.

thē girl and thē dog

thē girl said, "I can tēₐch thē dog to run."

thē dog said, "nō."

thē girl said, "I will tēₐch thē

dog to run."

   thē dog said, "nō. thē girl can

not tēₐch mē to run. I can run.

ha ha."

## lots of pots

a girl said, "that man has lots of
pots. hē has pots with tops. hē has
pots with nō tops."

the man said, "I haνe lots of cākes
in pots. I haνe a pot with a ship in it.
I haνe fish in pots."

the girl said, "can I hᾱve a pot fōr

a littlₑ fish?"

the man said, "this is a pot fōr a

littlₑ fish."

the girl said, "I will tākₑ this pot

hōmₑ with mē." and shē did.

36

a fish in the rāin

kim met pat in the rāin. kim got wet.

pat got wet.

kim said, "this is not fun."

pat said, "this is fun."

kim said, "I have wet fēēt. sō I

will gō hōme. I do not nēēd rāin."

pat said, "wē can get fish."

sō shē got a fish and gāve it to kim.

kim said, "it is fun to get wet if wē

get fish."

the cow on the rō<sub>a</sub>d

lots of men went in a littl<sub>e</sub> car. the

men went down a rō<sub>a</sub>d.

a cow sat on the rō<sub>a</sub>d. the cow did

not get up. sō the men ran to the cow.

the men said, "wē will lift this cow."

the men did not lift the cow. "this cow

is sō fat wē can not lift it."

the cow said, "I am not sō fat. I can

lift mē." the cow went in the car.

the men said, "now wē can not get

in the car." sō the men sat on the rōad

and the cow went hōme in the car.

the red hat

the fish had a car and nō hat. shē

said, "I do not nēēd a car. I nēēd a

red hat."

shē met a cow. the cow had a red hat.

the fish said, "can I have that red hat?"

the cow said, "nō."

the fish said, "I will give that cow a

car if shē will let mē have the hat."

the cow said, "tāke the hat and give

mē a car." sō the fish got a red hat

and the cow got a car.

a bug and a dog

a bug and a dog sat on a log. the

dog said, "that bug is sō littlₑ **I** can not

sēē him on the log."

the bug said, "**I** am big."

the dog said, "that bug on the log

is not big."

the bug said, "I will ēat this log."

and hē did. hē bit and bit and bit at the

log. the bug said, "now that dog can sēē

how big I am."

the dog said, "that bug can ēat logs

līke a big bug."

the bug bus

a little bug sat on the back of a big dog. "get down," said the dog. "I am not a bus."

the bug did not get down. shē went to sleēp. the dog said, "I am not a bed."

the dog ran to the pond and went in.

the bug got wet. the bug said, "I am not a fish. tāke mē back to the sand."

"nō," the dog said.

sō the bug said, "I will get mōre bugs on this dog." ten bugs cāme and got on the dog.

the dog said, "I fēēl līke a bug bus."

and the dog went back to the sand with

the bugs.

# the talking cat

the girl was gōīng fōr a walk. shē met a fat cat. "can cats talk?" the girl said.

the cat said, "I can talk. but I do not talk to girls. I talk to dogs."

the girl did not līke that cat. "I do not līke cats that will not talk to mē."

the cat said, "I will not talk to girls."

the girl said, "I do not līke that cat.

and I do not givₑ fish to cats I do not

līkₑ."

the cat said, "I līkₑ fish sō I will

talk to this girl." sō the girl and the cat

āte fish.

the rat got a sōre nōse

a rat and a rabbit went down a slīde.

the rabbit went down on his tāil. the

rat said, "I will gō down on the tāil."

the rat went up to the top of the slīde

and slid down on his nōse. hē said, "I

have a sōre nōse."

then hē said, "if a rabbit can gō down

on his tāil, I will do the sāme." hē went

up to the top. but hē cāme down on his

nōse.

the rabbit said, "that rat can not tell

if hē is on his nōse ōr his tāil."

the end

ron said, "yes"

ron's dad tōld him to slēēp in bed.

"yes," ron said. and hē did.

his mom said, "ron, pāint this bed red."

"yes," ron said. hē got the pāint and māde the bed red.

"that is fīne," his mom said.

a big boy met ron. hē said, "can ron

pāint a car red?"

"yes," ron said. and hē mā́de the car

red.

then ron went hōme. his mom said,

"ron mā́de a bed red and a car red. but

ron got lots of paint on ron. ron is red."

sō ron went to the tub and went rub,

rub, rub. now ron is not red.

this is the end.

hunting fōr a dēēr

ann said to her dad, "let's gō fīnd a dēēr fōr a pet."

sō ann and her dad went hunting fōr a dēēr. a dēēr cāme up to them. ann said, "you can bē a pet."

the dēēr said, "nō, a dēēr is not a pet.

dogs are pets. and cats are pets. I am

not a pet. but I will let a girl and her

dad pet mē."

the girl said, "that will bē fun." it was.

now, the girl has a pet dog and a pet

cat. they gō with her to hunt fōr the

dēēr that shē can pet.          the end

a card fōr mother →

a boy sent a card to his mother. the card said, "mother, I love you." but his mother did not get the card. →

a cop got the card. shē said, "I am not mother." sō shē gāve the card to her brother. →

her brother said, "this card is not

fōr mē. I am not mother."

sō the cop and her brother went to

fīnd mother. they met the boy.

the boy said, "you have the card that

I sent to mother. give mē that card."

sō they gāve him the card.

and hē gāve the card to his mother. ⟶

this is the end. ⟶

gōing to the toy shop

a boy and his mother went shopping fōr toys. the boy līked big toys. but his mother līked little toys.

the man in the toy shop said, "I havₑ toys that you will līkₑ. they arₑ big and little."

the boy said, "toys can not bē big and little."

the man said, "thēsₑ toys arₑ big and little."

hē got a little toy ᗪuck and hē mā́de it big.

this is the end.

the fat fox and her brother

a fat fox and her brother went into a big box.

the fat fox said, "I hāte to sit in a box."

her brother said, "sitting in a box is not a lot of fun. let's hit the box. I love to hit a box."

the fat fox said, "I will hit the box with this hand and this nōse and this tāil." sō shē hit and hit.

then the fat fox said, "it is getting hot in this

box. let's stop hitting."

her brother said, "let's gō to slēēp. slēēping in a

box is fun." sō they went to slēēp.

this is the end.

the pig that bit his leg

a little bug and a pig met on the rōₐd. the pig said, "I can walk better than you."

the little bug said, "but I can ēat better than you." then shē bit a log.

the pig said, "I can ēat logs better than you." the pig went bītₑ, bītₑ, bītₑ and ātₑ the log.

the bug said, "I can bītₑ a pig better than you."

shē bit the pig on the leg.

the pig said, "I can do better than that." the pig gāve his leg a big bīte.

the bug said, "you bīte pigs better than mē."

the end

the cat that talked

a girl had a little cat. shē loved her cat. shē went to the shop with her cat. shē went to the park with her cat. shē loved her cat.

the other dāy, shē was sitting with her cat in the park. shē said, "I love you, little cat. you are never bad. you are fun. but you can not talk to mē and that mākes mē sad."

the cat said, "I can talk to you."

stop

the cat that talked

a girl had a cat. she loved her cat. she talked to her cat.

then the cat talked to her. the girl said, "I must be sleeping. cats can not talk."

the cat said, "you talk to me. so I can talk to you."

the girl gave the cat a big hug. "I never had a

cat that talked."

the cat said, "I never had a cat that talked either." the girl and the cat talked and talked.

then ann came to the park. she went up to the girl and said, "can I have that cat?"

the cat said, "I will not go with you."

ann said, "I must be sleeping. cats do not talk. I will leave this park." and she did.

the end

the ōld man fīnds a hōrse

an ōld hōrse was in a barn. she said, "I am sad. I can not fīnd a man that will rīde on mē." she said to the cat, "have you seen a man that will rīde on mē?"

the cat said, "nō."

an ōld man was walking nēar the barn. he said to the cat, "I can not fīnd a hōrse to rīde. have you sēēn a hōrse that I can rīde?"

the cat said, "yes. shē is in the barn."

then the ōld man walked into the barn. hē went up to the ōld hōrse. the ōld man said, "ōld hōrse, do you līke to gō fōr a rīde?"

the ōld hōrse said, "yes." sō the ōld man and the ōld hōrse went rīding.

the end

rēₐd the Ītem ⟶

1. if the tēₐcher says "now," hōld up your hand. ⟶

bill went fishiñg ⟶

bill went fishiñg with the other boys. but hē did ⟶
not get fīve fish. hē did not get nīne fish. hē got ⟶
an ōld box. ⟶

the other boys māde fun of bill. "wē haveₑ fish ⟶
and you do not. you haveₑ an ōld box." ⟶

bill was sad. hē hit the box. the top fell down. and

bill said, "that box is filled with gōld."

bill was not sad. hē said to the other boys, "you

have lots of fish, but I have lots of gōld."

this is the end.

### rēad the Ītems

1. when the tēacher says "gō," pat your ēars.

2. when the tēacher says "do it," touch your fēēt.

### the red tooth brush

a girl had a red tooth brush. shē līked her red tooth brush. shē brushed her tēēth six tīmes a dāy. shē said, "mȳ tēēth are whīte. they are sō whīte they shīne līke the moon."

the girl had a dog, but his tēēth did not shīne.

the girl went to brush her tēēth. but shē did not sēē her tooth brush. "I do not sēē mȳ red tooth brush," shē said.

shē went to her mother. "I nēēd mȳ red tooth brush."

but her mother said, "I do not have your red tooth brush."

stop

## rēad the Items

1. when the tēacher says "stand up," pick up your book.

2. if the tēacher says "now," hōld up your hands.

## the red tooth brush

a girl līked to brush her tēēth. shē looked fōr her red tooth brush. but her mother did not have it. the girl went back to her room. on the wāy, shē slipped and fell. she slipped on her dog. her dog

was brushing his teeth with her red tooth brush.

the girl said, "you have my red tooth brush."

the dog said, "I like teeth that shine like the

moon."

the girl smiled and the dog smiled. they said,

"now we both have teeth that shine like the moon."

the end

rēₐd the Ītems →

1. if the tēₐcher stands up, touch your hand. →

2. if the tēₐcher says "stand up," touch your nōsₑ. →


the fat ēₐglₑ →

an ēₐglₑ lĪkₑd to ēat. hē ātₑ cākₑ and ham and →

cōrn. hē ātₑ and ātₑ, and hē got fatter and fatter. →

hē said, "I am sō fat that I can not flȳ." →

hē sat in a trēē and the other ēₐglₑs mādₑ fun of →

him. they said, "look at that fat, fat ēagle. hō, hō."

but then a tīger cāme hunting fōr ēagles. a little
ēagle sat under a trēē. the tīger went after the
little ēagle. the other ēagles yelled and yelled, but the
little ēagle did not hēar them.

stop

rēₐd the Ītems

1. when the tēₐcher says "touch your fēēt," stand

up.

2. if the tēₐcher says "gō," touch your ēₐrs.

the fat ēₐgle

a fat, fat ēₐgle was sittiñg in a trēē when a tīger

cāmₑ huntiñg fōr ēₐglₑs. the tīger went after a

little ēₐgle that was sittiñg under the trēē. the other

ēagles yelled, but the little ēagle did not hēar them.

the fat, fat ēagle looked down and said, "I must sāve the little ēagle." sō hē jumped from the trēē. hē cāme down līke a fat rock on the tīger. and the tīger ran far awāy.

now the other ēagles do not māke fun of the fat, fat ēagle. they give him cāke and ham and cōrn.

this is the end.